Guest Spot

CLASSIC BLUES
Playalong *for* Clarinet

WISE PUBLICATIONS
London/New York/Paris/Sydney/Copenhagen/Madrid

Exclusive Distributors:
Music Sales Limited
8/9 Frith Street, London W1V 5TZ, England.
Music Sales Pty Limited
120 Rothschild Avenue, Rosebery, NSW 2018, Australia.

Order No. AM941743
ISBN 0-7119-6266-9
This book © Copyright 1998 by Wise Publications.

Book design by Michael Bell Design.
Compiled by Peter Evans.
Music arranged by Jack Long & Paul Honey.
Music processed by Enigma Music Production Services.
Cover photography by George Taylor.

Printed in the United Kingdom by
Page Bros. Limited, Norwich, Norfolk.

CD recorded by Passionhouse Music.
Instrumental solos by John Whelan.
Produced by Paul Honey.

Your Guarantee of Quality:
As publishers, we strive to produce every book to
the highest commercial standards.
The music has been freshly engraved and the book has been
carefully designed to minimise awkward page turns and
to make playing from it a real pleasure.
Particular care has been given to specifying acid-free, neutral-sized
paper made from pulps which have not been elemental chlorine bleached.
This pulp is from farmed sustainable forests and was
produced with special regard for the environment.
Throughout, the printing and binding have been planned to
ensure a sturdy, attractive publication which should give years of enjoyment.
If your copy fails to meet our high standards,
please inform us and we will gladly replace it.

Music Sales' complete catalogue describes thousands of
titles and is available in full colour sections by subject,
direct from Music Sales Limited.
Please state your areas of interest and send a
cheque/postal order for £1.50 for postage to:
Music Sales Limited, Newmarket Road, Bury St. Edmunds, Suffolk IP33 3YB.

Visit the Internet Music Shop at
http://www.musicsales.co.uk

Guest Spot

Fingering Guide

Transposition

The B♭ clarinet sounds a major second below the written pitch.
Rule: Written C sounds B♭

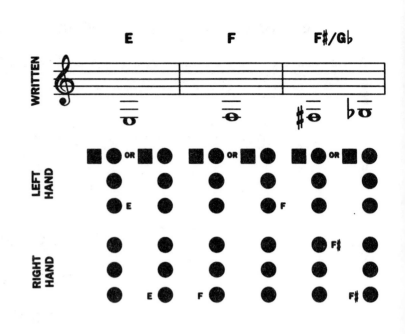

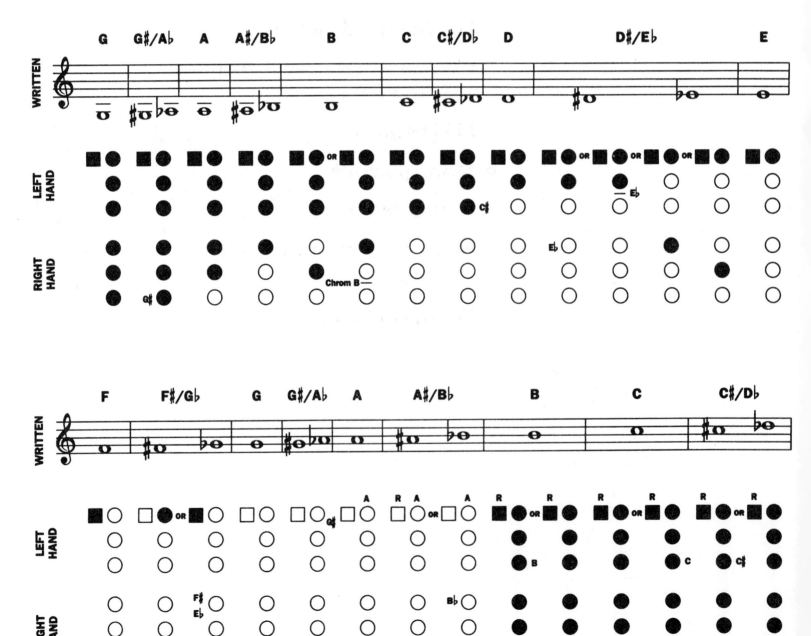

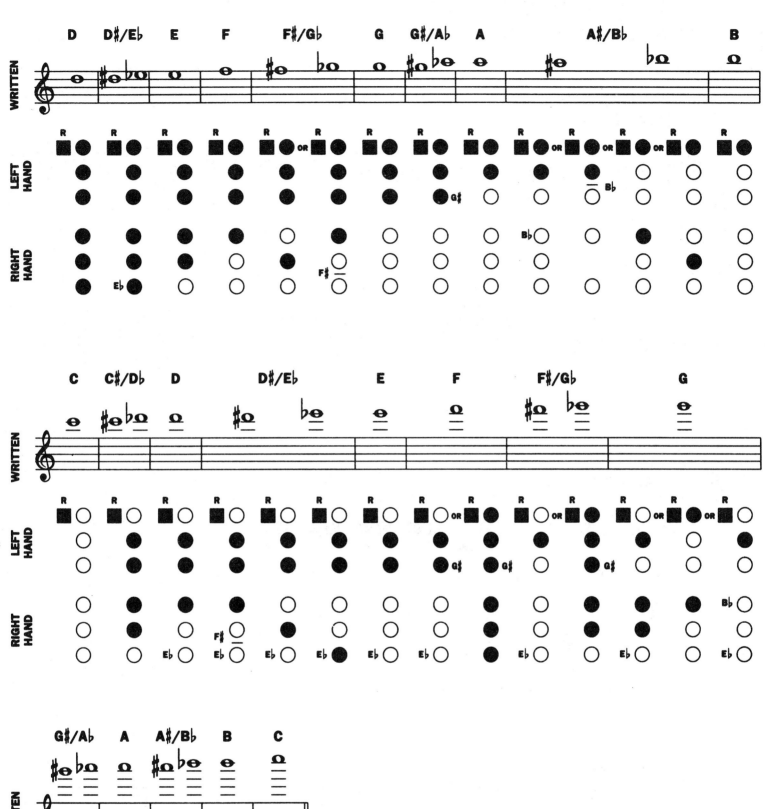
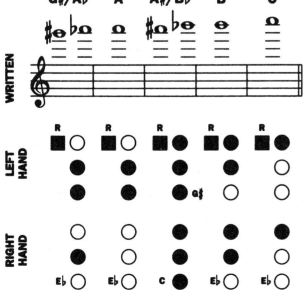

Cry Me A River

Words & Music by Arthur Hamilton

Slow ($\quarternote$ = 69)

Fever

Words & Music by John Davenport & Eddie Cooley

Medium tempo (♩ = 120)

To Coda ⊕

Swung ♪'s

D. %: al Coda

CODA

God Bless' The Child

Words & Music by Arthur Herzog Jr. & Billie Holiday

Slow medium (♩ = 78)

Li'l Darlin'

By Neal Hefti

D. %̸ al Coda

⊕ **CODA**

Harlem Nocturne

Music by Earle Hagen
Words by Dick Rogers

Hit The Road Jack

Words & Music by Percy Mayfield

Medium tempo (♩ = 126)

I Wish I Knew How It Would Feel To Be Free

By Billy Taylor

Medium tempo (♩ = 102)

To ⊕ *Coda*

D. % al Coda

⊕ **CODA**

Moonglow

Words & Music by Will Hudson, Eddie de Lange & Irving Mills

Swingin' Shepherd Blues

Words by Rhoda Roberts & Kenny Jacobson
Music by Moe Koffman

D.$ al Coda

CODA

Round Midnight

By Cootie Williams & Thelonious Monk

Slow ($\quarternote = 60$)

10/98 (32187)

The Beatles **Enya**

 Phil Collins **Van Morrison** **Bob Dylan**

 Sting **Paul Simon** **Tracy Chapman**

 Eric Clapton **Pink Floyd** **New Kids On The Block**

 **Bryan Adams** **Tina Turner** **Elton John**

 Bee Gees **Whitney Houston** **AC/DC**

Bringing you the
words

All the latest in rock and pop.
Plus the brightest and best in West
End show scores. Music books for
every instrument under the sun.
And exciting new teach-yourself
ideas like "Let's Play Keyboard" -
in cassette/book packs, or on video.
Available from all good music shops.

and
music

Music Sales' complete
catalogue lists thousands of
titles and is available free
from your local music shop,
or direct from Music Sales
Limited. Please send a
cheque or postal order for
£1.50 (for postage) to:

Music Sales Limited
Newmarket Road,
Bury St Edmunds,
Suffolk IP33 3YB

 **Buddy**  **Five Guys Named Moe** 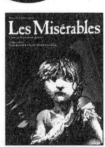 **Les Misérables**  **West Side Story**

 **Phantom Of The Opera**  **Show Boat**  **The Rocky Horror Show**

**Bringing you the
world's best music.**